Baby Book

I saw daylight for the first time on:

Date ....

....

Time ....

....

Place ....

....

....

My birth as told to me by my
mother

....
....
....
....
....
....
....
....
....
....
....
....
....
....
....
....

My weight when I was born

.... lbs. .... ozs. / .... kg .... g

My height when I was born

.... ins. .... cm

My first photograph

The colour of my eyes

....

The colour of my hair

....

The date I came home

.... / ....

The weather when I came home

....

....

....

....

....

My mother's notes on her stay in hospital

....
....
....
....
....
....
....
....
....
....
....
....
....
....

The date of my christening

.... / ....

The name of the church

....

My name

....

My Godparents

....

....

....

Photograph taken on the day
of my christening

A message from my godparents

....
....
....
....
....
....
....
....
....
....
....
....
....
....

A photograph of my godparents

My christening presents

....

....

....

....

....

....

....

....

....

....

....

....

....

My parents' notes on my christening

The names of my grandparents

....

....

....

....

My grandparents' notes
about me

....

....

....

....

....

....

....

....

....

....

....

....

....

....

My first lock of hair

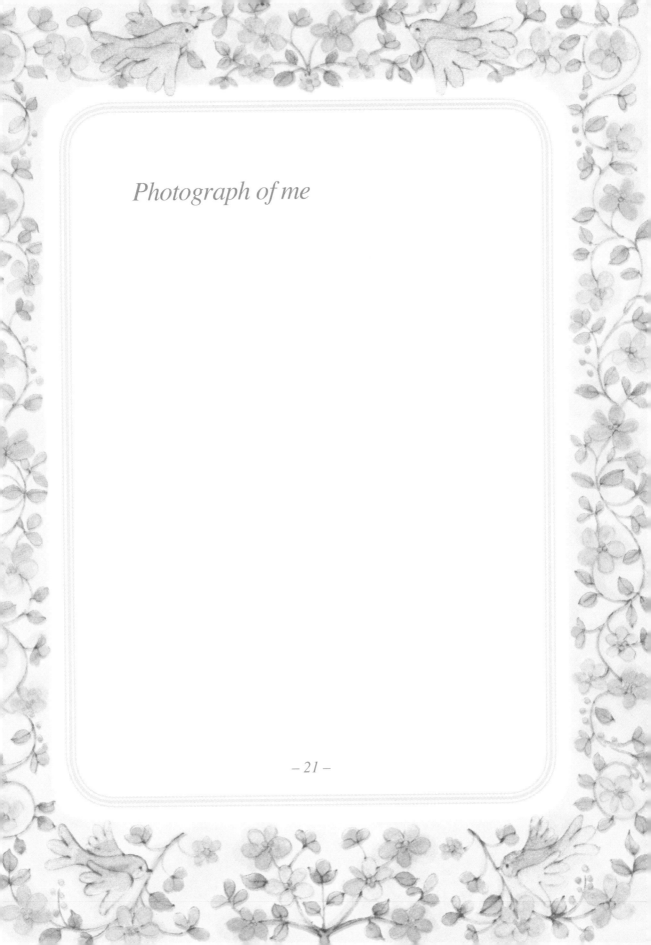

Photograph of me

My first home

....

....

....

....

....

Photograph of my first home

My first visits

My first visits

Illnesses

Name	Date

My parents' notes when
I was ill

....

....

....

....

....

....

....

....

....

....

....

....

....

Outline of my hand

Date .... /.......... ....

Outline of my foot

Date .... / ....

I first smiled on

I lifted my head on

I turned on to my stomach

I first laughed on

Date

....

....

....

....

My parents' notes

I first sat up on

I first held a toy on

I started crawling on

My first step was taken on

Date

....

....

....

....

My parents' notes

My first words

My parents' notes

*I first stood up
without help*

I start walking

Date

....

....

Photograph

My parents' notes

....

....

....

....

....

....

....

....

....

....

....

....

....

....

My first birthday party

Guests

....
....
....
....
....
....
....

Presents

....
....
....
....
....

My parents' notes

....

....

....

....

....

....

....

....

....

....

....

....

....

....

Photograph of me aged one

Photograph of me aged one

Development of my teeth

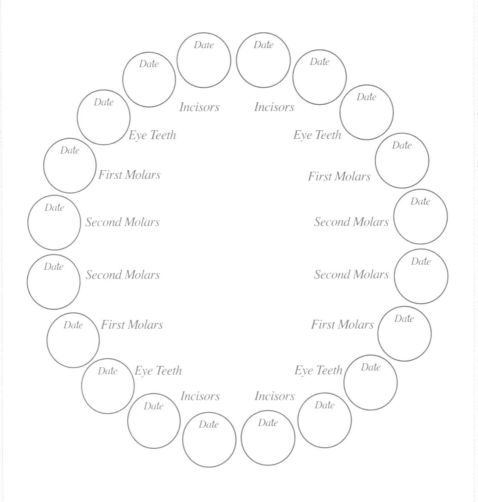

My parents' notes

....
....
....
....
....
....
....
....
....
....
....
....
....
....
....

My weight

Age:	Weight:
1 month	.... lbs .... ozs / ....kg .... g
2 months	.... lbs .... ozs / ....kg .... g
3 months	.... lbs .... ozs / ....kg .... g
4 months	.... lbs .... ozs / ....kg .... g
5 months	.... lbs .... ozs / ....kg .... g
6 months	.... lbs .... ozs / ....kg .... g
7 months	.... lbs .... ozs / ....kg .... g
8 months	.... lbs .... ozs / ....kg .... g
9 months	.... lbs .... ozs / ....kg .... g
10 months	.... lbs .... ozs / ....kg .... g
11 months	.... lbs .... ozs / ....kg .... g
1 year	.... lbs .... ozs / ....kg .... g
2 years	.... lbs .... ozs / ....kg .... g
3 years	.... lbs .... ozs / ....kg .... g
4 years	.... lbs .... ozs / ....kg .... g
5 years	.... lbs .... ozs / ....kg .... g
6 years	.... lbs .... ozs / ....kg .... g
7 years	.... lbs .... ozs / ....kg .... g

My parents' notes

....

....

....

....

....

....

....

....

....

....

....

....

....

My height

Age: Weight:

1 month   .... ins / .... cm

2 months   .... ins / .... cm

3 months   .... ins / .... cm

4 months   .... ins / .... cm

5 months   .... ins / .... cm

6 months   .... ins / .... cm

7 months   .... ins / .... cm

8 months   .... ins / .... cm

9 months   .... ins / .... cm

10 months   .... ins / .... cm

11 months   .... ins / .... cm

1 year   .... ft .... ins / .... m .... cm

2 years   .... ft .... ins / .... m .... cm

3 years   .... ft .... ins / .... m .... cm

4 years   .... ft .... ins / .... m .... cm

5 years   .... ft .... ins / .... m .... cm

6 years   .... ft .... ins / .... m .... cm

7 years   .... ft .... ins / .... m .... cm

My parents' notes

....
....
....
....
....
....
....
....
....
....
....
....
....
....

My first Christmas

My parents' notes

....

....

....

....

....

....

....

....

....

....

....

....

....

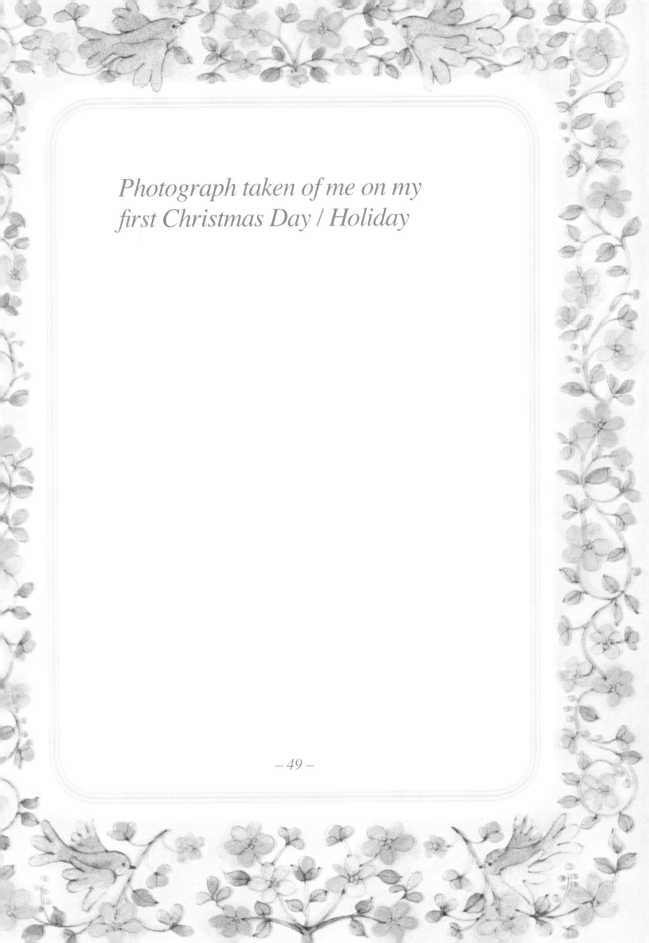

*Photograph taken of me on my
first Christmas Day / Holiday*

My favourite toys

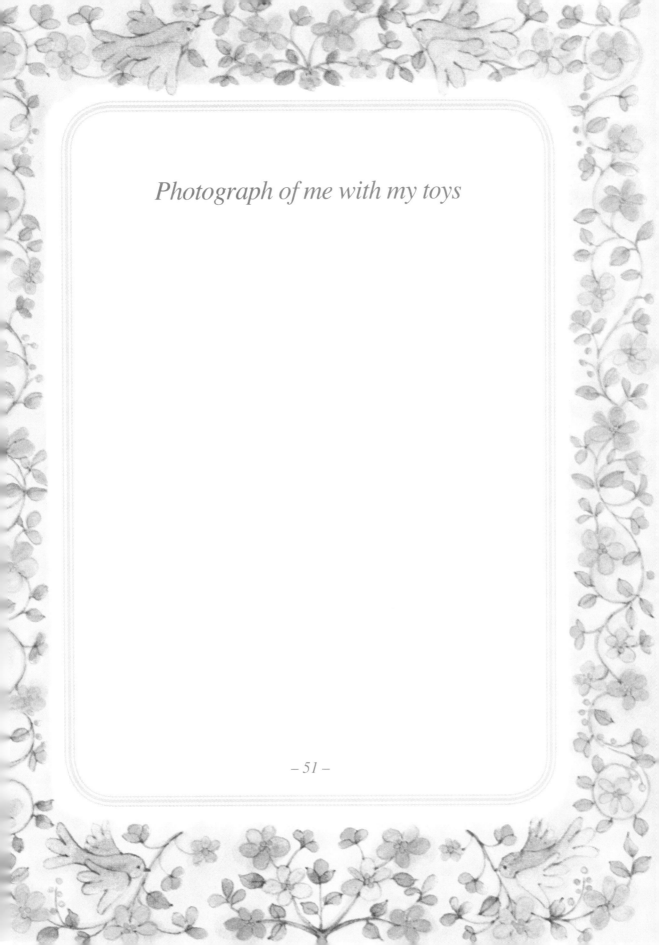

Photograph of me with my toys

My best friend when I was one

....

....

....

....

My best friend when I was two

....

....

....

....

My best friend when I was three

....

....

....

....

My best friend when I was four

....
....
....
....

My best friend when I was five

....
....
....
....

My best friend when I was six

....
....
....
....

My favourite stories

My second birthday party

Guests

....
....
....
....
....
....
....

Presents

....
....
....
....
....

Photograph of me aged two

My third birthday party

Guests

....
....
....
....
....
....
....

Presents

....
....
....
....
....

Photograph of me aged three

My fourth birthday party

Guests

....

....

....

....

....

....

....

Presents

....

....

....

....

....

Photograph of me aged four

My fifth birthday party

Guests

....
....
....
....
....
....
....

Presents

....
....
....
....
....

Photograph of me aged five

My sixth birthday party

Guests

....

....

....

....

....

....

....

Presents

....

....

....

....

....

Photograph of me aged six

My family tree

Father

Mother

Grandmother

Grandfather

Grandfather

Grandmother

Great Grandmother

Great Grandmother

Great Grandfather

Great Grandfather

Great Grandmother

Great Grandmother

Great Grandfather

Great Grandfather

My parents' notes

....
....
....
....
....
....
....
....
....
....
....
....
....
....
....

My first school

....

My first day at school

.... / ....

My first school friends

....

....

....

....

....

....

....

....

....

My parents' notes

Photographs of me on my first day at school

My favourite food

....
....
....
....
....
....
....
....
....
....
....
....
....
....

My least favourite food

My favourite games

My parents' notes

....

....

....

....

....

....

....

....

....

....

....

....

....

....

Drawings by me aged two

Drawings by me aged three

Drawings by me aged four

Drawings by me aged five

Drawings by me aged six

Drawings by me aged seven

My parents' comments on my
early years

....
....
....
....
....
....
....
....
....
....
....
....
....

My earliest childhood memories

....
....
....
....
....
....
....
....
....
....
....
....
....

Photographs

Photographs

Photographs

Contents